THE OFFICIAL NOTTS COUNTY QUIZ BOOK

THE OFFICIAL NOTTS COUNTY QUIZ BOOK

**Compiled by Chris Cowlin
and Kevin Snelgrove**

Foreword by Les Bradd

APEX PUBLISHING LTD

Hardback first published in 2008 by
Apex Publishing Ltd
PO Box 7086, Clacton on Sea, Essex, CO15 5WN, England
www.apexpublishing.co.uk

British Library Cataloguing-in-Publication Data
A catalogue record for this book
is available from the British Library

ISBN HARDBACK: 1-906358-37-0   978-1-906358-37-2

Typeset in 10.5pt Chianti Bdlt Win95BT

Cover Design: Siobhan Smith

Printed and bound in Great Britain by
Biddles Ltd., King's Lynn, Norfolk

Author's Note:
Please can you contact me: **ChrisCowlin@btconnect.com** if you find any
mistakes/errors in this book as I would like to put them right on any
future reprints of this book. I would also like to hear from Notts County
fans who have enjoyed the test! For more information on me and my
books please look at: **www.ChrisCowlin.com**

This book is an official product of Notts County Football Club.

We would like to dedicate this book to:

All the players and staff who have worked for the club during their history.

FOREWORD

It has been a privilege to be asked to provide this foreword for the official Notts County quiz book which I believe will give Notts County fans many hours of pleasure in testing their knowledge about Football's Oldest League Club.

I joined the Magpies in October 1967 following a £1,000 transfer from Rotherham United for a period that was to last nearly eleven years and be the happiest of my football career. I consider myself very fortunate to be one of a group of young players that manager Billy Gray signed for the Club in a bid to build a team good enough to win promotion. Unfortunately, Billy was unable to deliver the results and he left the Club unable to see players such as David Needham, Brian Stubbs, Bob Worthington and Don Masson all players he had signed become legends in the Club's history.

Jimmy Sirrel arrived as manager in 1969 and the Club went on to win promotion three times over the next ten years and achieved first division status in 1980/81. It was a pleasure to be part of the success story in the early seventies as the Club climbed two divisions and when my goal scoring achievements earned me the accolade as the Club's all time highest goal scorer. During this period we not only enjoyed promotions in the League but also great cup victories achieved against teams playing at higher levels. The Club also granted me a Testimonial year in 1977/78 and it was a year of many happy memories meeting supporters at darts nights, cabaret evenings and many other functions not least my testimonial game against Forest when over 11,000 fans attended the game for which I am extremely grateful.

It was a sad day for me when I was asked to leave the Club at the end of the 1977/78 season having made 441 first team appearances and scored 137 goals. I was transferred to Stockport County for the fee of £15,000 and went on to play for the Club for three years before moving on to Wigan Athletic for a further two seasons. I retired from playing in 1983 having made a total of 614 appearances and scoring 205 goals.

Following my retirement from playing football, I returned to Notts County to work in the Lottery Office and what a pleasure it was to be working for the Club whilst Neil Warnock was manager and the two occasions that he took the Club to Wembley to win successive promotions from the third to the first division.

I have thoroughly enjoyed working in football for most of my lifetime and have recently completed forty two years in the business. Nearly twenty five years have been spent at Notts County which I thought would help in answering questions in this book.

I am sure like me you will enjoy the 1,000 questions that Chris Cowlin has compiled covering everything a County fan would wish for including great matches, managers, players, transfers, goal scorers, league positions and much more.

I hope you have great fun with this book and remember for every sale of a copy of this book £1 will be donated to local Children's charities and to Education for the Children, a charity close to the heart of our former player Tommy Johnson.

Les Bradd

INTRODUCTION

I would first of all like to thank Les Bradd for writing the foreword to this book. Les is a true legend for County and I am very grateful for his help on this project.

I would also like to thank all the past legends of Notts County Football Club and many current employees of the club for their comments and reviews on this book (these can be found at the back of the book).

I would also like to thank Lynn Lawson for her help and advice during the books compilation.

I hope you enjoy this book. Hopefully it should bring back some wonderful memories!

It was great working with Kevin Snelgrove again, who is very well organised, between us I hope we have given you a selection of easy, medium and hard questions.

In closing, I would like to thank all my friends and family for encouraging me to complete this book.

Chris Cowlin

Best wishes
Chris Cowlin

Visit Chris Cowlin's website:

www.ChrisCowlin.com

Visit Kevin Snelgrove's website:

www.KevinSnelgrove.co.uk

HISTORY OF THE CLUB

1. In which year was the club formed – 1862, 1865 or 1868?

2. True or false: County are the oldest professional club?

3. What is the club's nickname that they share with Newcastle United?

4. Where do County play their home games?

5. Following on from the previous question, in which year did they move there?

6. Who is the club's highest all time goal scorer with 125 League goals?

7. Who holds the record for the most appearances in the League for County with 564 between 1904 and 1926?

8. Against which club did County record their highest cup victory in the FA Cup 1st round in October 1985?

9. The club recorded their highest attendance of 47,310 during March 1955 whilst playing York City, in what competition were they playing?

10. County have won the FA Cup once in their history, in which year – 1894, 1994 or 2004?

NATIONALITIES – 1

Match the player with their nationality

11.	Radojko Avramovic	Algerian
12.	Iain McCulloch	Serbian
13.	Shaun Goater	Welsh
14.	Paul Mayo	Australian
15.	Adem Poric	Trinidadian
16.	Tcham N'Toya	Scottish
17.	Youssef Sofiane	Irish
18.	Nigel Worthington	Bermudian
19.	Hector Sam	English
20.	Matthew Williams	French-Congolese

1990s

21. In which season did County win Division Three?

22. Who scored a hat-trick in the 4-1 home League win against Derby County at Meadow Lane during September 1993?

23. True or false: County played top-flight football during 1991-92 and were relegated finishing 21st in the League?

24. Which two players scored 29 goals between them during 1993-94?

25. In which position did County finish in Division Two during 1998-99?

26. Who managed the club between September 1994 and January 1995?

27. Who finished County's top scorer with 11 League goals during 1992-93?

28. Who scored a brace on the opening day of the 1998-99 season, against Oldham Athletic in a 3-1 away win?

29. Against which team did County record their biggest win of the 1992-93 season, a 5-1 home win in Division One during January 1993?

30. Who finished County's top scorer with nine League goals during 1994-95?

SQUAD NUMBERS – 1
2007-2008

Match the squad number to the player

31.	*Adam Tann*	*30*
32.	*Stef Frost*	*18*
33.	*Jay Smith*	*9*
34.	*Stephen Hunt*	*5*
35.	*Gavin Strachan*	*7*
36.	*Kevin Pilkington*	*4*
37.	*Mike Edwards*	*3*
38.	*Myles Weston*	*26*
39.	*Austin McCann*	*14*
40.	*Jason Lee*	*1*

WHERE DID THEY COME FROM? - 1

Match the team to the player

41.	Bobby Forrest	Sheffield United
42.	Paul Devlin	Bradford City
43.	Bill Baxter	Derby County
44.	Sam Haden	Rotherham United
45.	Mick Jones	Nottingham Forest
46.	Tony Agana	Arsenal
47.	Eric Probert	Stafford Rangers
48.	Chris With	Leeds United
49.	Garry Birtles	Burnley
50.	Chris Wilder	Nottingham Forest

MANAGERS

Match the seasons they were in charge to the manager

51.	Sam Allardyce	*1961-1963*
52.	Neil Warnock	*2002-2004*
53.	Howard Wilkinson	*1957-1958*
54.	Tom Harris	*1994-1995*
55.	Jimmy Sirrel	*1936-1937*
56.	Tommy Lawton	*1893-1913*
57.	Tim Coleman	*1969-1975*
58.	Russell Slade	*1982-1983*
59.	Bill Dearden	*1997-1999*
60.	Jimmy McMullan	*1989-1993*

INTERNATIONALS

Match the international caps whilst at County to the player

61.	Martin O'Neill	4 England caps
62.	Willie Davies	1 Republic of Ireland cap
63.	Henry Cursham	16 Northern Ireland caps
64.	Bert Morley	4 Republic of Ireland caps
65.	Arthur Green	8 England caps
66.	Kevin Wilson	5 Republic of Ireland caps
67.	Bill Fallon	1 England cap
68.	Tommy Lawton	5 Wales caps
69.	Eddie Gannon	6 Wales caps
70.	Ray O'Brien	8 Northern Ireland caps

LEAGUE APPEARANCES

Match the number of league appearances
they made for the club to the player

71.	David Hunt	347
72.	Albert Iremonger	407
73.	Pedro Richards	323
74.	George Smith	336
75.	Tristan Benjamin	395
76.	David Needham	564
77.	Alex Gibson	311
78.	Aubrey Southwell	429
79.	Percy Mills	399
80.	Les Bradd	328

81. Which two players scored goals in the 2-1 away win against Bradford City in the 1st round in August 2004?

82. Which Premier League team did County knock out in the 3rd round in October 1994, beating Ossie Ardiles' London team?

83. Following on from the previous question, can you name the two scorers in the game (one player scoring a brace)?

84. Which East Anglian side did County knock out in the 2nd round during September 2003 beating them 2-1 at home?

85. Who scored a hat-trick in the 4-3 away win against Mansfield Town during August 2001 in the 1st round?

86. Which London team did County beat 3-0 on aggregate in the 2nd round during September and October 1984?

87. True or false: County beat Newport County 5-0 in the 1st round during November 1971?

88. Can you name the two goal scorers in the 2-0 home win in the 3rd round during November 1982 against Chelsea?

89. Against which team was County's first ever League game in October 1960 in a 3-1 defeat with Harry Noon scoring?

90. Against which Midlands team did County play three replays in the 3rd round, eventually beating County 3-1 during December 1983?

GOALKEEPERS

91. Who kept 19 clean sheets during his 46 League appearances for County during 1995-96?

92. Which goalkeeper scored for County during August 2001 in the FA Cup?

93. Following on from the previous question, against which team did he score in a 4-3 away win?

94. How many clean sheets did Sean Deeney keep in his 49 appearances for County in his career?

95. Which goalkeeper clocked up 229 appearances for County between November 1972 and May 1979?

96. Who kept 183 clean sheets in his 564 appearances for the Magpies between April 1905 and May 1926?

97. When Mick Rose was injured against Crewe Alexandra in Division Four during October 1967, which defender and County captain went in goal for The Magpies?

98. Which goalkeeper scored for County in a 6-3 defeat against Leicester City in Division Two during September 1956?

99. Who made 323 appearances for County between November 1955 and April 1967?

100. Who started all 46 League matches for County during 1990-91?

POSITIONS IN DIVISION ONE

Match the position County finished to the season

101.	1898-99	37 points	10th
102.	1991-92	40 points	15th
103.	1925-26	33 points	14th
104.	1981-82	47 points	5th
105.	1905-06	34 points	18th
106.	1923-24	42 points	22nd
107.	1901-02	40 points	16th
108.	1910-11	38 points	3rd
109.	1892-93	24 points	21st
110.	1907-08	34 points	11th

HOME ATTENDANCES

Match the home attendance to the season

111.	1919-20	11,163
112.	1938-39	3.909
113.	2004-05	16,476
114.	1971-72	14,470
115.	1888-89	13,941
116.	1910-11	4,974
117.	2006-07	10,410
118.	1981-82	12,684
119.	1962-63	5,384
120.	1957-58	6,860

BIG WINS – 1

Match the big win against the team they beat in the season

121.	1974-75	v Hull City	6-2
122.	1927-28	v Barnsley	4-1
123.	1893-94	v Port Vale	9-1
124.	1949-50	v Newport County	5-0
125.	1921-22	v Leeds United	6-1
126.	1956-27	v Stoke City	7-1
127.	1987-88	v Southend United	0-5
128.	1886-87	v Sheffield	5-2
129.	1959-60	v Crystal Palace	9-0
130.	1966-67	v Luton Town	7-0

1999-2000

131. In which position did County finish in Division Two?

132. True or false: The Magpies were unbeaten in their first six League games?

133. Which manager started the season with Notts County but then left in October 1999?

134. Who finished the season as County's highest scorer with 13 League goals?

135. With which team did County share a 4-4 draw during November 1999?

136. Who scored County's only League hat-trick during this season?

137. Following on from the previous question, which team did he score against in a 5-1 home win during December 1999 with Ian Richardson and Mark Stallard also scoring?

138. True of false: County won every League game during October 1999?

139. Who scored a brace in the 3-2 away win against Oxford United during March 2000?

140. Who scored his only League goal of the season against Preston North End in a 1-0 win at Meadow Lane during March 2000?

WHO AM I? – 1

141. I finished the season with 17 League goals in only 20 appearances during 1954-55.

142. I signed from Plymouth Argyle in the late 1980s and left for Watford in the mid 1990s.

143. I made 103 League appearances for County scoring 31 goals during the early 1960s and was born in 1942.

144. I played for the club for 10 years and scored 125 League goals for the club.

145. I was born in Newcastle in January 1971, and made my debut in September 1988 at home to Preston North End.

146. I scored against Northampton Town on my debut during February 1937 in a 1-1 draw. I made 62 appearances and scored 15 League goals?

147. I was a fullback and made my League debut at Sunderland in a 3-0 defeat in 1974. I went on to play a total of 399 League appearances for The Magpies.

148. I was a centre forward and scored 109 League goals for County, I have a FA Cup finalist medal from 1967 and a Division Four Championship medal from 1971 which I gained with Notts County.

149. I had a goal scoring debut in a 4-4 draw (scoring twice for County) during August 1987 against Wigan Athletic. When I left County I joined Grimsby Town.

150. I managed The Magpies between January and April 1995.

LEAGUE GOALSCORERS

*Match the number of league goals they scored
for the club against the player*

151.	Ian McParland	97
152.	Tony Hateley	94
153.	Trevor Christie	69
154.	Les Bradd	58
155.	Mick Vinter	88
156.	Jackie Sewell	92
157.	Tom Johnston	63
158.	Harry Daft	109
159.	Tom Keetley	54
160.	Don Masson	125

CLEAN SHEETS

*Match the number of clean sheets they kept
or the club with the goalkeeper*

161.	Steve Cherry	44
162.	George Toon	38
163.	Darren Ward	75
164.	Mick Leonard	183
165.	Eric McManus	63
166.	Jimmy Ferguson	39
167.	Albert Iremonger	54
168.	Harry Pennington	41
169.	Roy Brown	66
170.	Gordon Bradley	74

BRIAN STUBBS

171. From which team did Brian join County in 1968?

172. What is Brian's middle name – Thomas, Harry or Henry?

173. In which position did Brian play during his playing days?

174. How many League appearances did Brian make for The Magpies – 486, 496 or 506?

175. What medal did Brian win in 1971 with County?

176. How many League goals did Brian score in his County career – 28, 29 or 30?

177. Against which Welsh based team did Brian make his County debut in a 3-0 home defeat?

178. Brian scored his first goal for County in January 1970 in a 5-2 away win against which Essex-based team?

179. How many League goals did Brian score for County during 1973-74 in his 32 appearances?

180. In March 1973 Brian scored the opening goal in the 3-0 home in against Halifax Town in Division Three. Which two other players scored in the game?

1980s

181. Who finished County's top League goal scorer during 1980-81?

182. Against which team did County record their biggest win during the 1982-83 season (5-1 home win)?

183. Who was County manager between June 1987 and December 1988?

184. Who scored a hat-trick for The Magpies on the opening day of the 1983-84 season in a 4-0 away win against Leicester City?

185. In which position did County finish in Division Three during 1986-87?

186. True or false: County scored nine goals in the first two League games of the 1987-88 season?

187. Which player scored a hat-trick in the 5-1 home win against Fulham during January 1988?

188. In which position did County finish in Division One during 1982-83?

189. Can you name the goal scorers in the 3-2 home League win against Manchester United during May 1983?

190. Who finished County's highest scorer with 15 League goals during 1984-85?

2000-2001

191. Which team did County beat 1-0 away on the opening day of the season with Mark Stallard scoring?

192. In what position did County finish in Division Two – 6th, 7th or 8th?

193. Who finished County's highest scorer with 17 League goals?

194. True or false: Two League hat-tricks were scored by Notts County players during this season?

195. Against which team did County record their biggest League win of the season, a 4-1 home win, during January 2001?

196. Following on from the previous question, can you name two of the four goal scorers who scored for The Magpies?

197. Who was County's manager during this season?

198. Who scored four League penalties during this season?

199. Which player finished this season with 13 League goals?

200. Which team did County beat 2-1 at home on the last day of the season with David Joseph and Mark Stallard scoring?

ANGLO-ITALIAN CUP
RUNNERS-UP 1994

201. Which Italian team did County play in the final?

202. What was the score in the final?

203. Who was in charge of The Magpies when they reached the final?

204. Which Essex-based side did County beat in the semi-final, drawing 1-1 on aggregate but then beating them 4-3 on penalties?

205. Following on from the previous question, which player scored County's goal in the semi-final?

206. Can you name two of the four Italian teams that County played before they reached the semi-finals?

207. Which English team did County beat 3-2 in August 1993, their first game of the competition?

208. Following on from the previous question, who scored a brace in the game?

209. Where was the final played – Wembley, Highbury or Villa Park?

210. Which goalkeeper played in all the Anglo-Italian matches?

NATIONALITIES – 2

Match the player with their nationality

211.	Duncan Jupp	Ivorian
212.	Cyril Hatton	French
213.	Ruben Zadkovich	Welsh
214.	Tony Scully	German
215.	Steve Scoffham	Scottish
216.	Fabrice Moreau	Irish
217.	Eugene Dadi	English
218.	Michael Emenalo	Nigerian
219.	Julien Baudet	Australian
220.	Lee Nogan	French-Cameroonian

MARK DRAPER

221. Mark was born on 11 November in which year –
1968, 1970 or 1972?

222. Where was Mark born – Long Ashton, Long Sutton or
Long Eaton?

223. In which year did Mark sign as a professional player
for The Magpies?

224. In which position does Mark play?

225. Mark made his County debut in a 0-0 draw against
which club?

226. In the 1992-93 season Mark was County's top League
scorer with how many goals?

227. How many League appearances did Mark make for
County – 212, 222 or 232?

228. How many League goals did Mark score in his six years
at the club?

229. Mark was transferred for £1.25 million in 1994 to
which club?

230. How many appearances for the England under-21
team did Mark make?

JEFF ASTLE

231. Jeff was born on 13 May in which year – 1942, 1944 or 1946?

232. Where was Jeff born – Westwood, Northwood or Eastwood?

233. At which club did Jeff start his professional football career?

234. In 1964 which club did Jeff transfer to for £25,000?

235. In the 1968 FA Cup final Jeff scored the goal in a 1-0 win against which team, which saw The Baggies lift the cup?

236. True or false: On the way to the 1968 FA Cup final Jeff scored in every round of the competition?

237. When Jeff was at West Bromwich Albion, what was his nickname?

238. In the 1969-70 season Jeff was the leading league goal scorer in Division One with how many goals?

239. In 1970 Jeff was called up for the England squad to play in the World Cup finals in Mexico, how many appearances did he make for the international team?

240. Jeff's England debut was as a substitute against which team?

SAM ALLARDYCE

241. Sam was born on 19 October in which year – 1954, 1956 or 1958?

242. Where was Sam born – Dudley, Daventry or Derby?

243. At which club did Sam start his professional playing career as a centre-half?

244. True or false: In 1977-78 Sam won the Second Division Championship. This is the only honour he has won as a player and a manger?

245. How many different teams did Sam play for in his career?

246. How many League appearances did Sam make in his career – 440, 445 or 450?

247. In which year did Sam take charge of Notts County?

248. In the 1997-98 season County became the first team since World War II to win the Division Three title and gain promotion in mid-March, how many points did they win the League by?

249. In 1999 Sam left The Magpies to manage which club?

250. On Wednesday 9 January 2008 Sam left which Premiership club by mutual agreement?

NEIL WARNOCK

251. Neil was born on 1 December in which year – 1944, 1946 or 1948?

252. Where was Neil born – Doncaster, Bradford or Sheffield?

253. At which club did Neil start his professional football career?

254. In Neil's eleven year playing career how many League appearances did he make – 316, 326 or 336?

255. True or false: Neil once owned a greengrocers shop in Barnsley called 'The Orange Bowl'?

256. How many years was Neil manager of County?

257. From 1990 to 1996 Warnock led three different teams to Wembley five times, how many finals did he win?

258. True or false: Neil is a fully qualified referee?

259. Which team did Neil manage in the Conference and took them into the football League in 1987?

260. Which team did Neil manage from 1999 to 2007?

WHERE DID THEY GO? – 1

Match the team to the player

261.	Gordon Wills	Derby County
262.	Brian Moore	Walsall
263.	Arthur Mann	Southend United
264.	Ian McParland	Leicester City
265.	Jason Cook	Hull City
266.	Dean Yates	Bristol City
267.	Tommy Lawton	Doncaster Rovers
268.	Richard Young	Northampton Town
269.	Paul Heffernan	Shrewsbury Town
270.	Mark Goodwin	Brentford

ANGLO-ITALIAN CUP
WINNERS 1995

271. Which Italian team did County beat in the final?

272. What was the score in the final?

273. Who scored the goals for County?

274. Where was the final played?

275. Which manager was in charge when the Magpies won the final?

276. Which English team did County draw 0-0 with both at home and away in both legs but then beat 3-2 on penalties?

277. Can you name two of the four teams that County played before reaching the semi-finals?

278. Who were the two goalkeepers that took part in the final match for County?

279. How many of County's six games before the final did they win – 1, 3 or 5?

280. True or false: County won this cup but were sadly relegated in the League?

CRAIG SHORT

281. Craig was born on 25 June in which year – 1968,
     1970 or 1972?

282. At which non-League club did Craig start his
     professional career?

283. Craig joined Notts County in 1989 from which club did
     he sign?

284. Craig made 128 League appearances for The Magpies
     how many league goals did he score?

285. True or false: Craig and his brother Chris played for the
     same club only once in their careers, which was
     County?

286. After spending four years with The Magpies Craig
     moved to Derby County for what was then a British
     record transfer fee for a defender. What was the fee?

287. In 1999 Craig joined which club for the transfer fee of
     £1.7 million?

288. When with Blackburn Rovers in 2001 Craig hit a brace
     in a 5-0 win against whom?

289. True or false: Craig missed the 2002 League Cup final
     through suspension, a match where Blackburn beat
     Tottenham 2-0?

290. After retiring from football Craig went to work at Lake
     Windermere. What is his business there?

MARTIN O'NEILL

291. Martin was born in Kilrea Northern Ireland on 1 March in which year – 1951, 1952 or 1953?

292. Can you name one of Martin's two nicknames?

293. At which club in 1971 did Martin start his professional football career, winning the Irish cup and scoring twice in the final?

294. In 1971 Martin joined which club where he went on to win Two League Championships, Two European Cups and the League Cup?

295. In which year did Martin join Notts County FC?

296. How many League appearances did Martin make for The Magpies – 60, 64 or 68?

297. Which club was Martin with when he decided to retire from playing football?

298. How many full international caps did Martin gain as a Northern Ireland player – 44, 64 or 84?

299. What award did Martin win in 2004 for his services to Football?

300. What award did Martin receive in November 2007?

WHERE DID THEY COME FROM? – 2

Match the team to the player

301.	Bob Worthington	Liverpool
302.	Paul Rideout	West Bromwich Albion
303.	William Ross	Southampton
304.	Dennis Pearce	Halifax Town
305.	Alf West	Kilmarnock
306.	Ray O'Brien	Dale Rovers
307.	George Smith	Middlesbrough
308.	Mick Leonard	Reading
309.	Iain McCulloch	Manchester United
310.	Kevin Bartlett	Wolverhampton Wanderers

2001-2002

311. Can you name two of the three managers who took charge during this season?

312. Who was County's top scorer with 19 League goals in 43 appearances?

313. True or false: County were unbeaten in the League during March 2002?

314. Against which team did The Magpies record their biggest win of the season, a 4-0 away win during March 2002?

315. Can you name the two goalkeepers that played for County this season?

316. Against which team did Danny Allsopp score a hat-trick in a 3-0 home win during March 2002?

317. How many goals did Darren Caskey score in his 42 League appearances this season?

318. In which position did County finish in Division Two?

319. Which team did County beat 2-1 on the last day of the season with Danny Allsopp and Kevin Nicholson scoring?

320. County's first win of the season came in their second match, a home game against which team with Craig Ireland and Mark Stallard scoring in a 2-1 win?

MATCH THE YEAR – 1

Match the year with the event

321.	Champions of Division Two and promoted to Division One?	1935
322.	Jackie Sewell transfers to Sheffield United for £34,500?	1890
322.	County reach the Third Division play-off semi-final, but lose to Walsall?	1994
324.	Ian Scanlon scores a hat-trick in less than three minutes?	1950
325.	Tommy Lawton reaches his century of league and cups goals?	2002
326.	Founder member of the Football league on 17 April?	1923
327.	Changed their kit colours back to Black and White strips?	1952
328.	The new all-seater stadium completed at Meadow Lane?	1888
329.	The club put into administration with debts exceeding £5 million?	1988
330.	Finished 3rd from bottom of the League and re-elected successfully?	1974

PEDRO RICHARDS

331.   In what position did Pedro play during his playing days?

332.   In which year was Pedro born in Edmonton – 1946, 1956 or 1966?

333.   In which year did Pedro make his debut for County?

334.   Following on from the previous question, against which North East team did Pedro make his debut in a 3-0 away defeat?

335.   What award did Pedro win at the end of the 1973-74 season?

336.   How many League appearances did Pedro make for County – 199, 299 or 399?

337.   How many League goals did Pedro score during his career with The Magpies – 1, 3 or 5?

338.   Which manager gave Pedro his County debut?

339.   Against which team did Pedro score his first League goal during April 1977 in a 3-1 home win?

340.   Against which team did Pedro score in a 6-1 League win during December 1983 with Trevor Christie, Nigel Worthington, Ian McParland and John Chiedozie (2) also scoring?

NOTTS COUNTY v NOTTINGHAM FOREST
COUNTY'S WINS IN DERBIES

Match the score to the date

341.	*12 February 1955 Division Two*	**3-0**
342.	*16 January 1886 Friendly*	**1-0**
343.	*18 September 1920 Division Two*	**4-2**
344.	*12 February 1994 Division One (new)*	**5-0**
345.	*30 August 1952 Division Two*	**5-1**
346.	*5 March 1881 Friendly*	**2-1**
347.	*17 March 1900 Division One*	**4-1**
348.	*1 May 1957 Division Two*	**3-0**
349.	*1 December 1883 FA Cup*	**3-2**
350.	*26 December 1883 Friendly*	**2-0**

CLUB TOP GOALSCORERS IN LEAGUE AND CUP

Match the number of goals to the correct player

351.	Tommy Lawton	90
352.	Tom Johnston	104
353.	Harry Daft	137
354.	Trevor Christie	92
355.	Les Bradd	114
356.	Tom Keetley	81
357.	Tony Hateley	97
358.	Ian McParland	79
359.	Don Masson	98
360.	Jackie Sewell	103

POSITIONS IN DIVISION TWO

Match the position County finished to the season/points

361.	1990-91 80 points	14th
362.	1956-57 30 points	6th
363.	1894-95 39 points	15th
364.	1913-14 53 points	18th
365.	1932-33 40 points	20th
366.	1976-77 48 points	1st
367.	1953-54 39 points	4th
368.	1904-05 18 points	17th
369.	1950-51 39 points	2nd
370.	1978-79 44 points	8th

DEAN YATES

371. In which year was Dean born in Leicester – 1960, 1967 or 1974?

372. In which position did Dean play during his playing days?

373. What award did Dean win in 1987 as a County player?

374. How many England under-21 caps did Dean win in his career – 1, 3 or 5?

375. How many League goals did Dean score in his County career – 33, 35 or 37?

376. Dean made his debut against Wimbledon at home during April 1985m what was the score?

377. How many League appearances did Dean make for County – 194, 294 or 394?

378. Which team did Dean join when he left County in 1995?

379. How many League goals did Dean score during 1986-87 in his 42 appearances for County?

380. Against which Welsh based side did Dean score the only goal in a 1-0 way win during April 1989 in Division Three?

2002-2003

381. Who finished County's highest League goal scorer with 24 goals?

382. Who managed The Magpies during this season?

383. In which position did County finish in the League – 15th, 16th or 17th?

384. Can you name the two players who scored 10 League goals each during this season?

385. Against which team did County record their biggest win of the season during September 2002, a 4-1 away win?

386. Following on from the previous question, can you name the two players who scored a brace in the game?

387. What was the only month in the season County were unbeaten?

388. Which team did County play of the opening day of the season, a 1-1 home draw during August 2002?

389. Which player scored his only League goal of the season against Blackpool in a 3-1 home win?

390. Can you name the three goalkeepers, which were used during this season, playing in County's 46 League matches?

PLAY-OFF WINNERS – 1989-1990

391.   Who guided County to this success?

392.   Which team did County play in the play-off final?

393.   What was the score in the final?

394.   Where was the game played?

395.   Which County players scored in the final?

396.   What was the attendance at the final – 19,252, 29,252 or 39,252?

397.   Can you name seven of the starting 11 who played for County in the final?

398.   Which team did County beat in the semi-finals?

399.   Following on from the previous question, what was the aggregate score – 2-1, 3-1 or 4-1?

400.   Who scored the goal in the semi-final, 1st leg in the 1-1 away draw?

LES BRADD

401. In which year was Les born in Buxton – 1945, 1946 or 1947?

402. How many appearances did Les make for Rotherham United before joining Notts County?

403. In which year did Les sign for the Magpies?

404. How many League goals did Les score in his Notts County career?

405. Which position did Les play during his playing career?

406. Against which team did Les score his first Notts County goal?

407. In which season did Les score 25 League goals in 53 games (all competitions) and win County player of the year?

408. Against which team did Les make his County debut in a 1-0 home win?

409. True or false: Les won a Division Four Championship medal with County in 1971?

410. Which team did Les join when he left The Magpies in August 1978?

DEBUTS

Match the appropriate debut to the player

411.   Craig Short

                                     Chester City (Home)
                                     August 2004, 1-1

412.   Frank Froggatt

                                     Reading (Away)
                                     September 1961, 2-4

413.   Trevor Christie

                                     Preston North End (Home),
                                     September 1988, 0-0

414.   Jeff Astle

                                     Sunderland (Away)
                                     January 2005, 2-1

415.   Robert Ullathorne

                                     Walsall (Home)
                                   March 1996, 2-1

416.   Tommy Johnson

                                     Darlington (Away)
                                   September 1968, 2-3

417.   Steve Finnan

                                     Barnsley (Home)
                                   November 1927, 9-0

418.   Glynn Hurst

                                     Blackpool (Home)
                                   August 1989, 0-1

419.   Steve Nicol

                                     Cardiff City (Home)
                                   August 1979, 4-1

420.   Bob Worthington

                                     Chester City (Home),
                                   August 2004, 1-1

TONY HATELEY

421. Tony was born on 13 June in which year – 1941, 1943 or 1945?

422. At which team did Tony start his professional career?

423. Tony made his debut for County on 8 November 1958 in a 1-1 draw where he scored, against which team?

424. How many League appearances did Tony make for The Magpies – 178, 188 or 198?

425. How many League goals did Tony score in his seven years at Notts County?

426. How many hat-tricks did Tony score while at County?

427. True or false: Tony's son is Mark Hateley who went on to play at international level for England?

428. After his first spell with County, in 1963 Tony left to join which Midlands rivals?

429. True or false: Hateley once scored five second half goals to bring his team back to draw 5-5?

430. Which manager took Tony to Anfield for £96,000 in 1967?

PRE-WORLD-WAR I AND II FA CUP WINS

Match the result to the season/round

431. 1921-22 Quarter-Final

County 2-0 Liverpool

432. 1935-36 2nd Round

Coventry City 0-2 County

433. 1906-07 3rd Round

Aston Villa 3-4 County

434. 1886-87 5th Round

County 2-0 Sunderland

435. 1890-91 Semi-Final Replay

Bolton Wanderers 1-4 County

436. 1938-39 3rd Round

County 4-0 Tottenham Hotspur

437. 1924-25 1st Round

County 3-1 Burnley

438. 1911-12 1st Round

County 5-2 Marlow

439. 1900-01 1st Round

County 3-0 Torquay United

440. 1893-94 Final

Luton Town 2-4 County

2003-2004

441. In which position did County finish in the League – 3rd, 13th or 23rd?

442. Can you name the two managers who were in charge during this season?

443. Who was County's highest scorer with 20 League goals in 38 League appearances?

444. True or false: County lost their first three games conceding 10 goals?

445. Which player scored four goals in the 4-1 home in during February 2004 against Stockport County at home?

446. Against which London club did Paul Heffernan score a League hat-trick on Boxing Day 2003 in a 3-3 home draw?

447. How many of The Magpies 46 League games did they win – 10, 20 or 30?

448. How many League goals did Darren Caskey score during this season – 1, 2 or 3?

449. Which player scored his only League goal in a 1-0 away win against Chesterfield during September 2003?

450. True or false: County scored in every League game during January 2004?

DON MASSON

451.   In which year was Don born – 1944, 1945 or 1946?

452.   At which club did Don start his professional career, playing 19 games for then in his career?

453.   For which country was Don a full international?

454.   How many international caps did Don win for his country – 7, 17 or 27?

455.   How many League goals did Don score for County in his career – 72, 82 or 92?

456.   Which Essex-based side did Don score a brace against on the last day of the 1968-69 season in a 2-0 home win?

457.   How many League goals did Don score during 1969-70 in his 43 League appearances?

458.   Against which team did Don made a scoring debut for The Magpies in a 3-2 away defeat during September 1968?

459.   Against which team did Don score a brace on 1 January 1974 in a 2-1 away win?

460.   How many League appearances did Don make for County – 402, 412 or 422?

HAT-TRICK HEROES

Match the player to the game they scored their hat-trick

461. v AFC Bournemouth (away)
      12 October 1961   Glynn Hurst
      League 3-2 win

462. v Tranmere Rovers (away)
      2 March 2002   Mick Vinter
      League 3-0 win

463. v Leeds City (away)
      24 January 1914   Tony Hateley
      League 4-2 win

464. v Manchester United (away)
      24 October 1931   David Hunt
      League 3-3 draw

465. v Crystal Palace (home)
      2 January 1960   Tom Johnston
      League 7-1 win

466. v Bristol City (home)
      12 October 1985   Billy Flint
      League 4-0 win

467. v Millwall (away)
      22 January 1977   Gary McSwegan
      League 5-2 win

468. v Watford (home)
      26 February 1949   Danny Allsopp
      League 4-0 win

469. v Bury (away)
      29 October 1905   Chris Joyce
      League 3-2 win

470. v Derby County (home)
      25 September 1993   Tom Keetley
      League 4-1 win

MARK STALLARD

471. Mark was born on 24 October in which year – 1970, 1972 or 1974?

472. Where was Mark born – Derby, Leicester or Coventry?

473. Which position does Mark play?

474. In 1991 at which club did Mark start his professional career?

475. On 3 March 1999 Mark joined Notts County for £10,000 from which club?

476. On 13 March 1999 Mark made his debut against York City, what was the result of this match?

477. In his two spells at The Magpies how many League appearances did Mark make – 164, 174 or 184?

478. Mark became a cult figure at Meadow Lane, how many League goals did he score?

479. Mark has score one hat-trick in his career this was in a 4-3 win for Wycombe Wanderers in October 1997, against which team?

480. In his first season with Lincoln City in 2006-07 how many goals did Mark score in all competitions?

MATCH THE YEAR – 2

Match the year to the event

481. German bombing damaged the
     pitch at Meadow Lane?   1987

482. A new stand opened at the County
     Road end of the ground   1962

483. The club turned professional?   1941

484. The first stage of the Meadow Lane
     stadium is rebuilt?   1910

485. Notts County football club celebrate
     their centenary?   1885

486. A crowd of 46,000 watched
     County v Forest?   1890

487. The last game is played at Trent
     Bridge, lost to Aston Villa 3-2?   1925

488. Derek Pavis took control of Notts
     County Football club?   1910

489. The club is nicknamed The Magpies?   1950

490. The first match is played at Meadow
     Lane against Nottingham Forest,
     the game ends in a 1-1 draw?   1992

TREVOR CHRISTIE

491. In which position did Trevor play during his playing days?

492. From which club did Trevor join The Magpies?

493. How many League goals did Trevor score for County in his career – 61, 62 or 63?

494. Against which team did Trevor make his County debut during August 1979 in a 4-1 home win?

495. True or false: Trevor scored on his County League debut?

496. How many League goals did Trevor score in his first season at Meadow Lane in 41 League appearances?

497. Against which team did Trevor score a hat-trick during April 1982 in a 4-1 home win?

498. Against which team did Trevor score a League hat-trick on the opening day of the 1983-84 season in a 4-0 away win?

499. Which manager signed Trevor for The Magpies?

500. Trevor signed for which team when he left County in July 1984?

GARY LUND

501. From which club did Gary join County in 1987?

502. How many League goals did Gary score in his County career – 62, 64 or 66?

503. Gary was originally a midfielder but then changed to which position?

504. Gary made his County debut during August 1987 against Wigan Athletic, what was the score in the game?

505. How many England under-21 caps did Gary win in his career?

506. Against which team did Gary score his first County goal during September 1987 in a 6-2 home win?

507. Against which team did Gary score a hat-trick in his first match at County during April 1988 in a 4-0 home win?

508. How many League appearances did Gary make for County – 248, 258 or 268?

509. How many League goals did Gary score in his first season at the club during his 40 appearances?

510. Against which team did Gary score the winner in a 2-1 away win on the opening day of the 1990-91 season?

GARY McSWEGAN

511. Gary was born on 24 September in which year –
      1968, 1970 or 1972?

512. Where was Gary born – Glasgow, Edinburgh or
      Dundee?

513. Gary joined Notts County in 1993 what was the
      transfer fee - £300,000, £350,000 or £400,000?

514. From which club did Gary join County?

515. Gary made his County debut on 14th August 1993 in a
      3-2 defeat to which club?

516. How many League appearances did Gary make for The
      Magpies – 52, 62 or 72?

517. How many League goals did Gary score in his two
      years at the club?

518. Gary was transferred from County for £375,000 in
      1995, which club did he join?

519. How many full international caps has Gary won for
      Scotland?

520. While playing for Scotland Gary only scored one goal
      against whom?

IAN McPARLAND

521. In which year did Ian take over as County manager?

522. Which team did Ian manage between February and May 2006?

523. How many League goals did Ian score in his County career – 69, 79 or 89?

524. Which manager gave Ian his County debut in 1980?

525. Following on from the previous question, against which team was County playing when Ian made his debut in the 2-2 away draw?

526. What is Ian's nickname?

527. What position did Ian play during his playing days?

528. Ian scored his first County League goal on 14 May 1983, against which side scoring the winning goal in a 3-2 home win?

529. How many League goals did Ian score for County in his 44 League appearances during 1985-86?

530. When Ian left County in 1988 which team did he join?

POSITIONS IN DIVISION THREE AND (D3 SOUTH)

Match the position they finished to the season/points

531.	1972-73 57 points	24th
532.	1986-87 76 points	13th
533.	1935-36 42 points	4th
534.	1961-62 43 points	2nd
535.	1989-90 87 points	23rd
536.	1948-49 43 points	12th
537.	1971-72 62 points	9th
538.	1963-64 27 points	3rd
539.	1946-47 40 points	11th
540.	1958-59 29 points	7th

2004-2005

541. Who finished County's highest goal scorer with 14 League goals?

542. What two managers were in charge during this season?

543. In which position did County finish in League Two?

544. Who scored the clubs only hat-trick during this season?

545. Following on from the previous question, against which team did he score during September 2004?

546. Can you name the three goal scorers in the 3-0 home win against Shrewsbury Town during November 2004?

547. Who scored a brace against Grimsby Town in a 2-2 home draw during April 1995?

548. County's highest League home attendance was 10,005 against which team in a 1-0 defeat during February 2005?

549. How many players were used during the League season?

550. County drew 0-0 at home with Rochdale but what was the score when County beat Rochdale at home earlier in the season?

DIVISION THREE CHAMPIONS – 1997-1998

551.   Who managed The Magpies during this season?

552.   How many players played in every League game during this season?

553.   How many of County's 46 League games did they win – 29, 31 or 33?

554.   Who was the Magpies top League goal scorer with 28 goals in 44 appearances?

555.   Who finished County's second highest scorer with 15 League goals in 35 appearances?

556.   Which team did County beat 5-3 away during January 1998 with Sean Farrell scoring a brace?

557.   Which striker scored twice in all of the last three League games of the season?

558.   Which team finished 2nd in the League, 17 points behind County?

559.   Who scored the only goal in the 1-0 home win against Hull City in January 1998?

560.   How many clean sheets did County keep during their 46 League games – 10, 15 or 20?

OVERALL TOP APPEARANCES

Match the number of appearances they made
for the club to the player

561.	Don Masson	442
562.	David Hunt	485
563.	Albert Iremonger	455
564.	David Needham	394
565.	Percy Mills	408
566.	Dean Yates	601
567.	Brian Stubbs	434
568.	Les Bradd	408
569.	Billy Flint	471
570.	Pedro Richards	486

STEVE FINNAN

571. Steve was born on 24 April in which year – 1974, 1976 or 1978?

572. Where was Steve born – Limerick, Waterford or Dublin?

573. Which non-League team did Steve play before turning professional?

574. From which team did Steve join County in 1996?

575. He made his County debut on 6th March 1996 in a 2-1 home win against which team?

576. In his two years at Notts County how many League appearances did Steve make – 60, 70 or 80?

577. In November 1998 Steve was transferred to Fulham, what was the fee?

578. In the summer of 2003 Steve made the move to which club for £3.5 million?

579. In the 2004-05 season for Liverpool Steve only scored one League goal in a 3-0 win against which team?

580. Who were Steve's first opponents in the Republic of Ireland shirt?

1970s

581. Who finished County's top goal scorer with 12 League goals in Division Two during 1978-79?

582. In which position did The Magpies finish in Division Two during 1976-77?

583. Which club did Dave Smith sign for when he left County in 1977?

584. Who was County's manager between 1975 and 1977?

585. In which year during the 1970s did Iain McCulloch make his debut for County having signed from Kilmarnock?

586. Can you name one of the only three players who played in all 46 League games during 1971-72?

587. In which position did The Magpies finish in Division Two during 1973-74?

588. True or false: Mick Vinter scored in six consecutive games during March and April 1978 in Division Two?

589. Which club did John Cozens sign for when he left County in 1972?

590. Which Scottish club knocked County out of the Anglo-Scottish Cup in the 1977-78 semi-final losing 2-1 on aggregate?

BRIAN KILCLINE

591.   Brian was born 7 May in which year – 1960, 1962 or 1964?

592.   Where was Brian born – Derby, Leicester or Nottingham?

593.   What is Brian's nickname?

594.   What position did Brian play?

595.   Brian signed for The Magpies in 1980, he made his debut on 6 October in a 3-2 win against which club?

596.   In Brian's four seasons at County how many League appearances did he make – 158, 162 or 166?

597.   How many League goals did Brian score during his time with County?

598.   In 1984 Brian moved to Coventry where in 1987 he captained them in the FA Cup final and eventually after extra-time winning 3-2, who did they beat in the final?

599.   True or false: In 1992 Brian was Kevin Keegan's first signing after taking over as the manager of Newcastle United?

600.   At which club did Brian finish his career only making two League appearances and scoring two League goals?.

WHERE DID THEY GO? – 2

Match the team to the player

601.	Craig Short	Bolton Wanderers
602.	Ron Wylie	Lincoln City
603.	Kevin Rapley	Leyton Orient
604.	Mick Waitt	West Bromwich Albion
605.	Ian Scanlon	Aston Villa
606.	George Taylor	Derby County
607.	Alec Simpson	Aberdeen
608.	Geoff Pike	Colchester United
609.	Harry Noon	Southampton
610.	Shaun Murphy	Bradford City

TOMMY JOHNSON

611. Tommy was born 15 January in which year – 1969, 1971 or 1973?

612. Where was Tommy born – Gateshead, Jarrow or Newcastle?

613. Tommy started his football career as a trainee at which club?

614. Tommy made his County debut on 26 August 1990 when County lost 1-0, to whom?

615. In Tommy's two years at The Magpies how many League appearances did he make – 112, 118 or 124?

616. How many League goals did Tommy score for County?

617. Which club did Tommy join from Notts County in 1992 staying three years and scoring almost a League goal every three games?

618. In 1997 Tommy moved to play north of the border in a £2.3million transfer. Which club did he join?

619. Tommy played at international level for the England under 21 team between 1990 and 1992 how many appearances did he make?

620. Tommy temporarily re-joined Notts County in November 2007 in what capacity?

THE MAGPIES' TRAINERS

Match the trainer to the period they worked at the club

621.	1986-89	Tom Prescott
622.	1929-34	David Lawson
623.	1893-1903	Dennis Pettit
624.	1948-56	Wayne Jones
625.	1992-94	Jack Wheeler
626.	1996-2004	Joe Goode
627.	1905-17	Tom Radcliffe
628.	1945-48	Bill Moore
629.	1994-96	Fred Banks
630.	1957-83	Roger Cleary

2007-2008

631. Who was County's manager during this season?

632. Which two players did County sign from Peterborough United during January 2008?

633. In which position did The Magpies finish in League Two – 19th, 21st or 23rd?

634. Who scored a last minute winner for County in a 2-1 win against Wrexham during October 2007?

635. How many of the clubs 46 League games did they win – 10, 15 or 20?

636. Which midfielder finished County's highest scorer with 12 League goals having played in all 46 League matches?

637. True or false: County drew their first four League matches?

638. Can you name the two scorers in the 2-1 home win against Shrewsbury Town during December 2007?

639. Which player left in July 2007 to join Bristol Rovers for £50,000?

640. Who scored the only goal in a 1-0 home win against Wycombe Wanderers during April 2008?

JOHN CHIEDOZIE

641. In which position did John play during his playing days?

642. From which London club did John join County in 1981?

643. John made his County debut in August 1981, against which team in a 1-0 away win?

644. John was County's record signing, how much did he cost the Magpies?

645. John scored his first goal in a 5-1 away win against which team in February 1982?

646. Against which North London team did John score a brace in March 1983 at Meadow Lane in a 3-0 win?

647. How many League goals did John score for County during 1982-83 in his 39 appearances in Division One?

648. How many League goals did John score in his County career – 16, 26 or 36?

649. For which country did John win 12 full international caps?

650. When John left County in August 1984 which top-flight team did he sign for?

PLAY-OFF WINNERS 1990-1991

651.   In which position did County finish in Division Two –
       3rd, 4th or 5th?

652.   Who managed The Magpies to this success?

653.   Where was the play-off final held?

654.   Which team did County play in the final?

655.   What was the score in the play-off final?

656.   Following on from the previous question, which County
       player scored a brace in the game?

657.   Which team did The Magpies beat 2-1 on aggregate in
       the semi-finals?

658.   Who scored the goals in the semi-final, 2nd leg, that
       put County through in the 1-0 win?

659.   True or false: County won their last seven League
       games to reach the play-offs?

660.   Tommy Johnson finished the season with 16 League
       goals, but how many play-off goals did he score in the
       three play-off matches?

WHO AM I? – 2

661. I made my debut in August 1979 in a 4-1 win against Cardiff City. I was County player of the year during 1982-83 and I was born in Yugoslavia.

662. I was born in October 1968, I played in midfield and I made my County debut away at Oldham in a 3-1 win during August 1998.

663. I took over as manager at Meadow Lane in October 1958 and left in November 1961 when Tim Coleman took over.

664. I was player of the year during 1985-86, I scored five League goals for County in my career and I made my debut in April 1975 away against West Bromwich Albion.

665. I was born in 1964 in London, I was a centre forward and made my debut in September 1990 against Bristol Rovers, winning 3-2 at home. I scored 17 League goals in 56 games during my time with The Magpies.

666. I was County's highest scorer during 1996/1997 with 6 League goals and I made my County debut during March 1996 in a 1-0 defeat at Blackpool.

667. I scored a hat-trick against Newport County during February 1961 in a 6-0 home win. I made 121 League appearances scoring 22 goals during my time with The Magpies.

668. I was player of the year during 1990-91, I played as a central defender and was born in 1968.

669. I was County's highest League goal scorer with 15 goals during 2006-07?

670. I was player of the year during 1999-2000, I made my debut against Exeter City during March 1998 in a 5-2 away win.

CLUB HONOURS
Match the season to the club honour

671. Division Three South Champions   1990-91

672. FA Cup Runners-up   1970-71

673. Promoted to Division Two via the play-offs   1993-94

674. Division Three Champions   1930-31

675. Division Four Champions   1994-95

676. FA Cup Winners   1890-91

677. Anglo-Italian Cup Runners-up   1893-94

678. Division Two Champions   1997-98

679. Promoted to Division One via the play-offs   1989-90

680. Anglo-Italian Cup Winners   1913-14

THE MAGPIES ON TOUR

Notts County Football Club played 47 tour matches W25, L10, D12 between 1910 and 2003. Can you match the year to the Country they toured?

681.	Kenya	1922
682.	Slovakia	1954
683.	Denmark	1984
684.	Italy	1946
685.	Spain	1994
686.	The Far East	1925
687.	Gibraltar	1999
688.	Central Europe	1910
689.	Holland	1971
690.	Germany	1975

2005-2006

691. Who finished County's highest scorer with nine League goals during his 18 appearances?

692. In which position did County finish in League Two?

693. True or false: County were unbeaten during August 2005 in their first six League games?

694. Who scored a hat-trick in the 3-2 away win against Bury during October 2005?

695. Who managed The Magpies during this season?

696. Who was the only player to play in every League game of the season (all 46 matches)?

697. Kevin Pilkington played in 45 League matches, missing one, who stepped in when he missed the game?

698. Which two players scored the goals in the 2-2 draw against Mansfield Town during March 2006?

699. True or false: County were unbeaten during April 2006?

700. What was the score on the last day of the season, at home to Bury?

POT LUCK

701. Who was County's Player of the Season during 2006-07?

702. Who won seven Northern Ireland under-21 caps during the 2004-05 and 2005-06 seasons whilst at County?

703. In which season did County set a record and won 30 League matches out of 46?

704. Who became County's 1,000th player when he made a substitute appearance in November 2006?

705. Who was County's Player of the Season during 1972-73?

706. Who scored a hat-trick for County in just 2 minutes, 45 seconds during November 1974 against Sheffield Wednesday in a 3-3 draw?

707. What was the score when County played Newquay away from home in a friendly during June 2002 – 10-1, 15-1 or 20-1?

708. Who was County's Player of the Season during 1997-98?

709. In which position did County finish in Division Four during 1959-60 – 1st, 2nd of 3rd?

710. Who managed the club between January 1989 and January 1993?

POST WORLD-WAR II FA CUP WINS

Match the result to the season/round

711.   1947-48 3rd Round   **Watford 1-4 County**

712.   1978-79 3rd Round   **Charlton Athletic 0-2 County**

713.   1954-55 5th Round   **Birmingham City 0-2 County**

714.   1949-50 2nd Round   **County 2-1 Blackburn Rovers**

715.   2007-08 1st Round   **Stoke City 0-2 County**

716.   1991-92 4th Round   **County 1-0 Chelsea**

717.   1964-65 1st Round   **County 4-2 Reading**

718.   1971-72 3rd Round   **County 3-0 Histon**

719.   1985-86 3rd Round   **County 2-0 Chelmsford City**

720.   1977-78 3rd Round   **Rochdale 1-2 County**

CLUB RECORDS

721. The highest attendance at Meadow Lane was 47,310 on 12 March 1955 in the FA Cup 6th round where County lost 1-0, to whom?

722. Who made the most League appearances for County, a staggering 564?

723. County's record League victory took place on 15 January 1949 in the Division Three South against Newport County what was the score?

724. The club record FA Cup win came in the 1st round on 24 October 1985 a 15-0 drubbing of whom?

725. In the season of 1959-60 Notts County scored a club record number of League goals in Division Four. How many goals did they score?

726. Who is County's highest scorer in one season, in the Division Three South 1930-31 he scored 39 goals?

727. The highest gate receipts of £124,539 were taken in the FA Cup 6th round match on 16th February 1991. Who were County playing?

728. Who is the all time top scorer in the league with 124 goals?

729. In 1997-98 Division Three how many points did County end the season with a club record?

730. The lowest post World War II attendance record was against Brighton & Hove Albion in Division Three on 3 December 1997. What was the attendance?

DIVISION TWO RUNNERS-UP
– 1980-1981

731. Can you name one of the three players who played in every one of the 42 League games?

732. Who managed County during this season?

733. How many of County's 42 League games did they win – 8, 18 or 28?

734. Which London team won the League being 13 points ahead of The Magpies?

735. Who was County's highest scorer with 14 League goals in 39 League appearances?

736. Ian McParland scored how many goals in 39 League appearances?

737. Against which team did County record their biggest League win, a 4-2 home win during September 1980?

738. Which two teams beginning with 'C' did County beat 2-0 during their last two League games?

739. Who two players scored the goals on the opening day of the season, a 2-1 home win against Bolton Wanderers?

740. True or false: County were unbeaten in the League during February 1981?

TOMMY LAWTON

741. Tommy was born on 6 October in which year – 1917, 1919 or 1921?

742. Where was Tommy born – Farnworth, Bletchworth or Lulworth?

743. At which club did Tommy start his professional career?

744. From which club did he join The Magpies in 1947 for £20,000?

745. Tommy made his County debut on 15 November 1947 in a 2-1 win against whom?

746. How many League appearances did Tommy make for County – 141, 151 or 161?

747. How many League goals did Tommy score for The Magpies bettering one goal every two games?

748. In October 1938 Tommy made his England debut away in a 4-2 defeat, though he did score a penalty, who were England's opponents?

749. How many international appearances did Tommy make for his Country?

750. Tommy managed Notts County for one season, which season?

1960s

751. Who was County's highest scorer with 27 League goals during 1960-61 in Division Three?

752. Who was County's manager between November 1961 and July 1963 and then again between April 1965 and March 1966?

753. Who scored a hat-trick in a 4-2 home win against Oldham Athletic during December 1963?

754. County's biggest win of the 1961-62 season was a 8-1 win against which team during September 1961 in Division Three?

755. From which club did County sign Terry Thompson in 1965?

756. Who scored a hat-trick during September 1964 in a 5-1 home win against Chesterfield?

757. In which season during the 1960s were County relegated from Division Three to Division Four?

758. In which position did County finish in Division Four during 1964-65?

759. Which two players scored double figures in the League during 1966-67, one scoring 12 and the other 10?

760. Can you name the only player that played in every League game during 1966-67?

SQUAD NUMBERS – 2
2007-2008
Match the squad number to the player

761.	Lawrie Dudfield	11
762.	Lee Canoville	21
763.	Rob Austin	12
764.	Neil MacKenzie	10
765.	Gary Silk	15
766.	Tim Sandercombe	6
767.	Paul Mayo	17
768.	Matthew Somner	2
769.	Andy Parkinson	20
770.	Spencer Wier-Daley	8

YEARS AT THE CLUB

Match the season to the player's time at the club

771.	Gary Lund	1910-22
772.	Les Bradd	1929-33
773.	Tommy Lawton	1968-82
774.	Don Masson	1987-95
775.	Mark Stallard	1885-95
776.	Sam Richards	1967-78
777.	Jimmy Oswald	1972-79
778.	Mick Vinter	1998-2005
779.	Harry Daft	1947-52
780.	Tom Keetley	1889-93

BIG WINS – 2

Match the big win with the team they beat in the season

781.	1917-18 v Grimsby Town	1-7
782.	1949-50 v Leyton Orient	4-0
783.	1962-63 v Colchester United	7-0
784.	1874-75 v Newark	1-5
785.	1916-17 v Hull City	4-1
786.	1923-24 v Chelsea	5-1
787.	1970-71 v Stockport county	0-6
788.	1979-80 v Cardiff City	8-0
789.	1947-48 v Reading	7-1
790.	1983-84 v Wolverhampton Wanderers	6-0

2006-2007

791. True or false: County were unbeaten in their first five League games?

792. Who was The Magpies highest League scorer with 15 goals?

793. Against which team did County record their biggest League win of the season, a 5-2 home win during January 2007?

794. Following on from the previous question, who scored a brace in the game?

795. How many players were used during the League season – 25, 30 or 35?

796. In which position did County finish in League Two – 11th, 12th or 13th?

797. Who was the Magpies manager during this season?

798. Who scored a brace in the 3-2 home win against Accrington Stanley during September 2006?

799. Which team were County playing when they had their highest home attendance of the season, 10,034, with the game ending up a 0-0 draw during March 2007?

800. How many of County's 46 League games did they win?

ANSWERS

HISTORY OF THE CLUB

1. 1862
2. True
3. The Magpies
4. Meadow Lane
5. 1910
6. Les Bradd
7. Albert Iremonger
8. Rotherham Town
9. FA Cup (6th round)
10. 1894

NATIONALITIES – 1

11.	Radojko Avramovic	Serbian
12.	Iain McCulloch	Scottish
13.	Shaun Goater	Bermudian
14.	Paul Mayo	English
15.	Adem Poric	Australian
16.	Tcham N'Toya	French-Congolese
17.	Youssef Sofiane	Algerian
18.	Nigel Worthington	Irish
19.	Hector Sam	Trinidadian
20.	Matthew Williams	Welsh

1990s

21. 1997/1998
22. Gary McSwegan
23. True
24. Mark Draper (14) and Gary McSwegan (15)
25. 16th
26. Russell Slade
27. Mark Draper
28. Sean Farrell
29. Tranmere Rovers
30. Paul Devlin

SQUAD NUMBERS – 1 2007-2008

31.	Adam Tann	5

32.	Stef Frost	14
33.	Jay Smith	7
34.	Stephen Hunt	18
35.	Gavin Strachan	26
36.	Kevin Pilkington	1
37.	Mike Edwards	4
38.	Myles Weston	30
39.	Austin McCann	3
40.	Jason Lee	9

WHERE DID THEY COME FROM? – 1

41.	Bobby Forrest	Leeds United
42.	Paul Devlin	Stafford Rangers
43.	Bill Baxter	Nottingham Forest
44.	Sam Haden	Arsenal
45.	Mick Jones	Derby County
46.	Tony Agana	Sheffield United
47.	Eric Probert	Burnley
48.	Chris With	Bradford City
49.	Garry Birtles	Nottingham Forest
50.	Chris Wilder	Rotherham United

MANAGERS

51.	Sam Allardyce	1997-1999
52.	Neil Warnock	1989-1993
53.	Howard Wilkinson	1982-1983
54.	Tom Harris	1893-1913
55.	Jimmy Sirrel	1969-1975
56.	Tommy Lawton	1957-1958
57.	Tim Coleman	1961-1963
58.	Russell Slade	1994-1995
59.	Bill Dearden	2002-2004
60.	Jimmy McMullan	1936-1937

INTERNATIONALS

61.	Martin O'Neill	8 Northern Ireland caps
62.	Willie Davies	6 Wales caps
63.	Henry Cursham	8 England caps

64.	Bert Morley	1 England cap
65.	Arthur Green	5 Wales caps
66.	Kevin Wilson	16 Northern Ireland caps
67.	Bill Fallon	5 Republic of Ireland caps
68.	Tommy Lawton	4 England caps
69.	Eddie Gannon	1 Republic of Ireland cap
70.	Ray O'Brien	4 Republic of Ireland caps

LEAGUE APPEARANCES

71.	David Hunt	336
72.	Albert Iremonger	564
73.	Pedro Richards	399
74.	George Smith	323
75.	Tristan Benjamin	311
76.	David Needham	429
77.	Alex Gibson	347
78.	Aubrey Southwell	328
79.	Percy Mills	407
80.	Les Bradd	395

THE LEAGUE CUP

81. Robert Ullathorne and Ian Richardson
82. Tottenham Hotspur
83. Gary McSwegan and Tony Agana
84. Ipswich Town
85. Danny Allsopp
86. Charlton Athletic
87. False: the score was 6-0 to County
88. Trevor Christie and Paul Hooks
89. Brighton & Hove Albion
90. Birmingham City

GOALKEEPERS

91. Darren Ward
92. Steve Mildenhall
93. Mansfield Town
94. 14
95. Eric McManus

96.   Albert Iremonger
97.   Alex Gibson
98.   Gordon Bradley
99.   George Smith
100. Steve Cherry

POSITIONS IN DIVISION ONE

101.	1898-99	37 points	5th
102.	1991-92	40 points	21st
103.	1925-26	33 points	22nd
104.	1981-82	47 points	15th
105.	1905-06	34 points	16th
106.	1923-24	42 points	10th
107.	1901-02	40 points	3rd
108.	1910-11	38 points	11th
109.	1892-93	24 points	14th
110.	1907-08	34 points	18th

HOME ATTENDANCES

111.	1919-20	16,476
112.	1938-39	10,410
113.	2004-05	5,384
114.	1971-72	13,941
115.	1888-89	3,909
116.	1910-11	12,684
117.	2006-07	4,974
118.	1981-82	11,613
119.	1962-63	6,860
120.	1957-58	14,470

BIG WINS – 1

121. 1974-75 v Hull City 0-5
122. 1927-28 v Barnsley 9-0
123. 1893-94 v Port Vale 6-1
124. 1949-50 v Newport County 7-0
125. 1921-22 v Leeds United 4-1
126. 1957-57 v Stoke City 5-0
127. 1987-88 v Southend United 6-2

128.	1886-87 v Sheffield 9-1
129.	1959-60 v Crystal Palace 7-1
130.	1966-67 v Luton Town 5-2

1999-2000

131.	8th
132.	True: Four wins and two draws
133.	Sam Allardyce
134.	Mark Stallard
135.	Bristol City
136.	Brett Angell
137.	Bournemouth
138.	False: They won their first five games and lost the last one 1-0 against Brentford
139.	Andy Hughes
140.	Matt Redmile

WHO AM I? – 1

141.	Jimmy Jackson
142.	Steve Cherry
143.	Jeff Astle
144.	Les Bradd
145.	Tommy Lawson
146.	Cyril Hatton
147.	Pedro Richards
148.	Tony Hateley
149.	Gary Birtles
150.	Howard Kendall

LEAGUE GOALSCORERS

151.	Ian McParland	69
152.	Tony Hateley	109
153.	Trevor Christie	63
154.	Les Bradd	125
155.	Mick Vinter	54
156.	Jackie Sewell	97
157.	Tom Johnston	88
158.	Harry Daft	58

| 159. | Tom Keetley | 94 |
| 160. | Don Masson | 92 |

CLEAN SHEETS

161.	Steve Cherry	75
162.	George Toon	63
163.	Darren Ward	74
164.	Mick Leonard	54
165.	Eric McManus	66
166.	Jimmy Ferguson	44
167.	Albert Iremonger	183
168.	Harry Pennington	39
169.	Roy Brown	41
170.	Gordon Bradley	38

BRIAN STUBBS

171. Loughborough United
172. Henry
173. Central Defender
174. 486: 483 (3)
175. Division Four Championship Medal
176. 28
177. Swansea Town
178. Southend United
179. Six
180. Jon Nixon and Les Bradd

1980s

181. Trevor Christie
182. Coventry City
183. John Barnwell
184. Trevor Christie
185. 7th
186. True: 4-4 (Wigan Athletic - home) and 5-3 (York City – away)
187. Ian McParland
188. 15th
189. Rachid Harkouk (2) and Ian McParland
190. Rachid Harkouk

2000-2001

191. **Luton Town**
192. **8th**
193. **Mark Stallard**
194. **False: no hat-tricks were scored**
195. **Rotherham**
196. **Anders Jacobsen, Richard Liburd, Andy Hughes and Mark Stallard**
197. **Jocky Scott**
198. **Danny Allsopp**
199. **Danny Allsopp**
200. **Oxford United**

ANGLO-ITALIAN CUP RUNNERS-UP 1994

201. **Brescia**
202. **0-1**
203. **Mick Walker**
204. **Southend United**
205. **Paul Devlin**
206. **Ascoli, Pisa, Brescia and Ascona**
207. **Derby County**
208. **Andy Legg**
209. **Wembley**
210. **Steve Cherry**

NATIONALITIES – 2

211. **Duncan Jupp** — Scottish
212. **Cyril Hatton** — English
213. **Ruben Zadkovich** — Australian
214. **Tony Scully** — Irish
215. **Steve Scoffham** — German
216. **Fabrice Moreau** — French-Cameroonian
217. **Eugene Dadi** — Ivorian
218. **Michael Emenalo** — Nigerian
219. **Julien Baudet** — French
220. **Lee Nogan** — Welsh

MARK DRAPER

221.   1970
222.   Long Eaton
223.   1988
224.   Midfield
225.   Wolverhampton Wanderers
226.   11
227.   222
228.   41
229.   Leicester City
230.   Three

JEFF ASTLE

231.   1942
232.   Eastwood
233.   Notts County
234.   West Bromwich Albion
235.   Everton
236.   True
237.   'The King'
238.   25
239.   5
240.   Brazil

SAM ALLARDYCE

241.   1954
242.   Dudley
243.   Bolton Wanderers
244.   No – He also won the Division Three Championship with Notts County in 1998
245.   Nine
246.   445
247.   1997
248.   19 points
249.   Bolton Wanderers
250.   Newcastle United

NEIL WARNOCK

251. 1948
252. Sheffield
253. Chesterfield
254. 326
255. True
256. Four
257. Four
258. True
259. Scarborough
260. Sheffield United

WHERE DID THEY GO? – 1

261.	Gordon Wills	Leicester City
262.	Brian Moore	Doncaster Rovers
263.	Arthur Mann	Shrewsbury Town
264.	Ian McParland	Hull City
265.	Jason Cook	Northampton Town
266.	Dean Yates	Derby County
267.	Tommy Lawton	Brentford
268.	Richard Young	Southend United
269.	Paul Heffernan	Bristol City
270.	Mark Goodwin	Walsall

ANGLO-ITALIAN CUP WINNERS 1995

271. Ascoli
272. 2-1
273. Tony Agana and Devon White
274. Wembley Stadium
275. Steve Nicol
276. Stoke City
277. Ascoli, Lecce, Atalanta and Venezia
278. Steve Cherry and Paul Reece
279. One: They drew five
280. True

CRAIG SHORT

281. 1968

282. Pickering Town

283. Scarborough

284. Six

285. False – He was with his brother at three clubs, Pickering, Scarborough and County

286. £2.5 million

287. Blackburn Rovers

288. Burnley

289. True

290. Sailing

MARTIN O'NEILL

291. 1952

292. 'Aston Martin' or 'Midas'

293. Distillery FC

294. Nottingham Forest

295. 1983

296. 64

297. Notts County

298. 64

299. OBE

300. FA Premier League Manager of the Month

WHERE DID THEY COME FROM? – 2

301.	Bob Worthington	Middlesbrough
302.	Paul Rideout	Southampton
303.	William Ross	Reading
304.	Dennis Pearce	Wolverhampton Wanderers
305.	Alf West	Liverpool
306.	Ray O'Brien	Manchester United
307.	George Smith	Dale Rovers
308.	Mick Leonard	Halifax Town
309.	Iain McCulloch	Kilmarnock
310.	Kevin Bartlett	West Bromwich Albion

2001-2002

311. Jocky Scott, Gary Brazil and Bill Dearden

312. Danny Allsopp

313. *True: Five wins and one draw*

314. *Bury*

315. *Stuart Garden and Steve Mildenhall*

316. *Tranmere Rovers*

317. *Five*

318. *19th*

319. *Huddersfield Town*

320. *Cambridge United*

MATCH THE YEAR – 1

321. *1923*

322. *1950*

323. *1988*

324. *1974*

325. *1952*

326. *1888*

327. *1935*

328. *1994*

329. *2002*

330. *1890*

PEDRO RICHARDS

331. *Full-back*

332. *1956*

333. *1974*

334. *Sunderland*

335. *Supporters reserve team player of the year*

336. *399: 397 (2)*

337. *Five*

338. *Jimmy Sirrel*

339. *Southampton*

340. *Sunderland*

COUNTY'S WINS IN DERBIES

341. *4-1*

342. *5-0*

343. *2-0*

344. *2-1*

345. 3-2
346. 1-0
347. 3-0
348. 4-2
349. 3-0
350. 5-1

CLUB TOP GOALSCORERS

351.	Tommy Lawton	103
352.	Tom Johnston	92
353.	Harry Daft	81
354.	Trevor Christie	79
355.	Les Bradd	137
356.	Tom Keetley	98
357.	Tony Hateley	114
358.	Ian McParland	90
359.	Don Masson	97
360.	Jackie Sewell	104

POSITIONS IN DIVISION TWO

361. 4th
362. 20th
363. 2nd
364. 1st
365. 15th
366. 8th
367. 14th
368. 18th
369. 17th
370. 6th

DEAN YATES

371. 1967
372. Central defender
373. Player of the year award
374. Five
375. 37
376. 2-3

377. 394: 392 (2)
378. Derby County
379. Nine
380. Cardiff City

2002-2003

381. Mark Stallard
382. Bill Dearden
383. 15th
384. Danny Allsopp and P____ Heffernan
385. Cheltenham Town
386. Mark Stallard and Danny Allsopp
387. May: played one and won one
388. Wycombe Wanderers
389. Craig Ireland
390. Stuart Garden, Steve Mildenhall and Saul Deeney

PLAY-OFF WINNERS – 1989-1990

391. Neil Warnock
392. Tranmere Rovers
393. 2-0 to Notts County
394. Wembley Stadium
395. Tommy Johnson and Craig Short
396. 29,252
397. Steve Cherry, Charlie Palmer, Nicky Platnauer, Craig Short, Dean Yates, Phil Robinson, Dean Thomas, Phil Turner, Kevin Bartlett, Gary Lund and Tommy Johnson
398. Bolton Wanderers
399. 3-1: 1-1 and 2-0
400. Gary Lund

LES BRADD

401. 1947
402. Four
403. 1967
404. 125
405. Centre forward
406. Rochdale

407.   1971/1972
408.   Crewe Alexandra
409.   True
410.   Stockport County

DEBUTS

411.	Craig Short	Blackpool (Home)
		August 1989, 0-1
412.	Frank Froggatt	Barnsley (Home)
		November 1927, 9-0
413.	Trevor Christie	Cardiff City (Home)
		August 1979, 4-1
414.	Jeff Astle	Reading (Away)
		September 1961, 2-4
415.	Robert Ullathorne	Chester City (Home)
		August 2004, 1-1
416.	Tommy Johnson	Preston North End (Home)
		September 1988, 0-0
417.	Steve Finnan	Walsall (Home)
		March 1996, 2-1
418.	Glynn Hurst	Chester City (Home)
		August 2004, 1-1
419.	Steve Nicol	Sunderland (Away)
		January 2005, 2-1
420.	Bob Worthington	Darlington (Away)
		September 1968, 2-3

TONY HATELEY

421.   1941
422.   Notts County
423.   Stockport County
424.   188
425.   109
426.   Seven
427.   True
428.   Aston Villa
429.   False: Four second half goals
430.   Bill Shankly

PRE-WORLD WAR I AND II FA CUP WINS

431.   Aston Villa 3-4 County

432.   County 3-0 Torquay United

433.   County 4-0 Tottenham Hotspur

434.   County 5-2 Marlow

435.   County 2-0 Sunderland

436.   County 3-1 Burnley

437.   Coventry City 0-2 County

438.   Luton Town 2-4 County

439.   County 2-0 Liverpool

440.   Bolton Wanderers 1-4 County

2003-2004

441.   23rd

442.   Bill Dearden and Gary Mills

443.   Paul Heffernan

444.   True

445.   Paul Heffernan

446.   Queens Park Rangers

447.   10

448.   Two

449.   Paul Bolland

450.   True

DON MASSON

451.   1946

452.   Middlesbrough

453.   Scotland

454.   17

455.   92

456.   Colchester United

457.   23

458.   Darlington

459.   Sunderland

460.   402

HAT-TRICK HEROES

461.   Tony Hateley

462. **Danny Allsopp**

463. **Billy Flint**

464. **Tom Keetley**

465. **Chris Joyce**

466. **David Hunt**

467. **Mick Vinter**

468. **Tom Johnston**

469. **Glynn Hurst**

470. **Gary McSwegan**

MARK STALLARD

471. **1974**

472. **Derby**

473. **Striker**

474. **Derby County**

475. **Wycombe Wanderers**

476. **Notts County 4-2 York City**

477. **184**

478. **69**

479. **Walsall**

480. **17**

MATCH THE YEAR – 2

481. **1941**

482. **1925**

483. **1885**

484. **1992**

485. **1962**

486. **1950**

487. **1910**

488. **1987**

489. **1890**

490. **1910**

TREVOR CHRISTIE

491. **Centre forward**

492. **Leicester City**

493. **63**

494.	*Cardiff City*

495.	*False*

496.	*Nine*

497.	*Brighton & Hove Albion*

498.	*Leicester City*

499.	*Jimmy Sirrel*

500.	*Nottingham Forest*

GARY LUND

501.	*Lincoln City*

502.	*62*

503.	*Centre forward*

504.	*4-4*

505.	*Three*

506.	*Southend United*

507.	*Rotherham United*

508.	*248: 223 (25)*

509.	*20*

510.	*Hull City*

GARY MCSWEGAN

511.	*1970*

512.	*Glasgow*

513.	*£400,000*

514.	*Rangers*

515.	*Middlesbrough*

516.	*62*

517.	*21*

518.	*Dundee United*

519.	*Two*

520.	*Lithunania*

IAN McPARLAND

521.	*2007*

522.	*Nottingham Forest*

523.	*69*

524.	*Jimmy Sirrel*

525.	*Preston North End*

526. Charlie

527. Centre forward

528. Manchester United

529. 15

530. Hull City

POSITIONS IN DIVISION THREE AND (D3-SOUTH)

531. 2nd

532. 7th

533. 9th

534. 13th

535. 3rd

536. 11th

537. 4th

538. 24th

539. 12th

540. 23rd

2004-2005

541. Glynn Hurst

542. Gary Mills and Ian Richardson

543. 19th

544. Glynn Hurst

545. Rochdale

546. Paul Bolland, Glynn Hurst and Chris Palmer

547. Stefan Oakes

548. Mansfield Town

549. 30

550. 3-0

DIVISION THREE CHAMPIONS – 1997-1998

551. Sam Allardyce

552. Zero

553. 29

554. Gary Jones

555. Sean Farrell

556. Lincoln City

557. Gary Jones

558. Macclesfield Town
559. Ian Richardson
560. 15

OVERALL TOP APPEARANCES

561. Don Masson   455
562. David Hunt   408
563. Albert Iremonger 601
564. David Needham   471
565. Percy Mills   434
566. Dean Yates   394
567. Brian Stubbs   486
568. Les Bradd   442
569. Billy Flint   408
570. Pedro Richards   485

STEVE FINNAN

571. 1976
572. Limerick City
573. Welling United
574. Birmingham City
575. Walsall
576. 80
577. £600,000
578. Liverpool
579. West Bromwich Albion
580. Greece

1970s

581. Mick Vinter
582. 8th
583. Torquay United
584. Ron Fenton
585. 1978
586. Les Bradd, Jon Nixon and Bob Worthington
587. 10th
588. True: Mansfield (home), Hull City (away), Bolton Wanderers (home), Brighton & Hove Albion (away), Fulham (home) and

Millwall (home)
589. Peterborough United
590. St. Mirren

BRIAN KILCLINE

591. 1962
592. Nottingham
593. 'Killer'
594. Centre half
595. Bristol Rovers
596. 158
597. Nine
598. Tottenham Hotspur
599. True
600. Halifax Town

WHERE DID THEY GO? – 2

601. Craig Short   Derby County
602. Ron Wylie   Aston Villa
603. Kevin Rapley   Colchester United
604. Mick Waitt   Lincoln City
605. Ian Scanlon   Aberdeen
606. George Taylor   Bolton Wanderers
607. Alec Simpson   Southampton
608. Geoff Pike   Leyton Orient
609. Harry Noon   Bradford City
610. Shaun Murphy   West Bromwich Albion

TOMMY JOHNSON

611. 1971
612. Gateshead
613. Notts County
614. Blackpool
615. 118
616. 47
617. Derby county
618. Celtic
619. Seven

620.   Coaching Staff

THE MAGPIES' TRAINERS

621.   Wayne Jones
622.   Fred Banks
623.   Joe Goode
624.   Bill Moore
625.   David Lawson
626.   Roger Cleary
627.   Tom Prescott
628.   Tom Radcliffe
629.   Dennis Pettit
630.   Jack Wheeler

2007-2008

631.   Ian McParland
632.   Guy Branston and Gavin Strachan
633.   21st
634.   Neil MacKenzie
635.   10
636.   Richard Butcher
637.   True
638.   Krystian Pearce and Neil MacKenzie
639.   David Pipe
640.   Richard Butcher

JOHN CHIEDOZIE

641.   Winger
642.   Leyton Orient
643.   Aston Villa
644.   £450,000
645.   Coventry City
646.   Tottenham Hotspur
647.   Five
648.   16
649.   Nigeria
650.   Tottenham Hotspur

PLAY-OFF WINNERS 1990-1991

651.   4th

652.   Neil Warnock

653.   Wembley

654.   Brighton & Hove Albion

655.   3-1 to Notts County

656.   Tommy Johnson

657.   Middlesbrough

658.   Paul Harding

659.   True

660.   Two (in the final)

WHO AM I? – 2

661.   Raddy Avramovic

662.   Gary Owers

663.   Frank Hill

664.   Tristan Benjamin

665.   David Regis

666.   Gary Martindale

667.   Alan Withers

668.   Craig Short

669.   Jason Lee

670.   Alex Dyer

CLUB HONOURS

671.   1930-31

672.   1890-91

673.   1989-90

674.   1997-98

675.   1970-71

676.   1893-94

677.   1993-94

678.   1913-14

679.   1990-91

680.   1994-95

THE MAGPIES ON TOUR

681.   Kenya   1984

682.	Slovakia	1994
683.	Denmark	1910
684.	Italy	1971
685.	Spain	1922
686.	The Far East	1999
687.	Gibraltar	1975
688.	Central Europe	1925
689.	Holland	1954
690.	Germany	1946

2005-2006

691. Glynn Hurst
692. 21st
693. True: Four wins and two draws
694. Hlynn Hurst
695. Gudjon Thordarson
696. Mike Edwards
697. Shaun Marshall
698. Chris Palmer and Daniel Chillingworth
699. False: Drew three and lost three
700. 2-2

POT LUCK

701. Mike Edwards
702. Emmet Friars
703. 1970-71
704. Jay Smith
705. Roy Brown
706. Ian Scanlon
707. 15-1
708. Garry Jones
709. 2nd
710. Neil Warnock

POST WORLD-WAR II FA CUP WINS

711. Birmingham City 0-2 County
712. County 4-2 Reading
713. County 1-0 Chelsea

714.   Rochdale 1-2 County

715.   County 3-0 Histon

716.   County 2-1 Blackburn Rovers

717.   County 2-0 Chelmsford City

718.   Watford 1-4 County

719.   Stoke City 0-2 County

720.   Charlton Athletic 0-2 County

CLUB RECORDS

721.   York City

722.   Albert Iremonger

723.   11-1

724.   Rotherham Town

725.   107

726.   Tom Keetley

727.   Manchester City

728.   Les Bradd

729.   99 points

730.   1,279

DIVISION TWO RUNNERS-UP – 1980-1981

731.   Tristan Benjamin, David Hunt and Brian Kilcline

732.   Jimmy Sirrel

733.   18

734.   West Ham United

735.   Trevor Christie

736.   11

737.   Cardiff City

738.   Chelsea and Cambridge United

739.   Trevor Christie and Paul Hooks

740.   True: Three wins and One draw

TOMMY LAWTON

741.   1919

742.   Farnworth, Lancashire

743.   Burnley

744.   Chelsea

745.   Northampton Town

746.	151
747.	90
748.	Wales
749.	23
750.	1957-58

1960s

751.	Tony Hateley
752.	Tim Coleman
753.	Jeff Astle
754.	Newport County
755.	Wolverhampton Wanderers
756.	Jim Raynor
757.	1963-64
758.	13th
759.	Stan Marshall (12) and Terry Harkin (10)
760.	Alex Gibson

SQUAD NUMBERS – 2 2007-2008

761.	Lawrie Dudfield	10
762.	Lee Canoville	2
763.	Rob Austin	17
764.	Neil MacKenzie	8
765.	Gary Silk	12
766.	Tim Sandercombe	20
767.	Paul Mayo	15
768.	Matthew Somner	6
769.	Andy Parkinson	11
770.	Spencer Wier-Daley	21

YEARS AT THE CLUB

771.	Gary Lund	1987-95
772.	Les Bradd	1967-78
773.	Tommy Lawton	1947-52
774.	Don Masson	1968-82
775.	Mark Stallard	1998-2005
776.	Sam Richards	1910-22
777.	Jimmy Oswald	1889-93

778.	Mick Vinter	1972-79
779.	Harry Daft	1885-95
780.	Tom Keetley	1929-33

BIG WINS – 2

781.	1917-18 v Grimsby Town	8-0
782.	1949-50 v Leyton Orient	1-7
783.	1962-63 v Colchester United	0-6
784.	1874-75 v Newark	7-0
785.	1916-17 v Hull City	7-1
786.	1923-24 v Chelsea	6-0
787.	1970-71 v Stockport county	1-5
788.	1979-80 v Cardiff City	4-1
789.	1947-48 v Reading	5-1
790.	1983-84 v Wolverhampton Wanderers	4-0

2006-2007

791.	True: Two wins and three draws
792.	Jason Lee
793.	Torquay United
794.	Jason Lee
795.	25
796.	13th
797.	Steve Thompson
798.	Dan Martin
799.	Mansfield Town
800.	16: Eight home and eight away

NOTES

NOTES

NOTES

NOTES

NOTES

NOTES

NOTES

NOTES

NOTES

NOTES